Superman and the Robots

In this comic you will meet ...

Superman
The most powerful superhero ever!

Mr White
The boss at the newspaper. He likes to shout – a lot!

Clark Kent
A newspaper reporter. He has a secret ...
but can he keep it?

Lois Lane
The star reporter at the newspaper.

Jimmy Olsen
A young boy who works at the newspaper.

Superboy, Supergirl and Superdog
Superman's super family!

From deep in space, a huge meteorite is crashing towards Earth ...
Oh no! It's heading towards the city!
But wait! What is that?
LOOK!
What is that, up in the sky?
Is it a bird?
Is it a plane?

No!
Look at that!
It's Superman!
Yes – and he's only using one hand!
Wow! He really *is* super!
He stopped that meteorite from falling on us!
My hero!

Back at the newspaper, the boss is angry!

Sorry I'm late, Boss! Did I miss something?
PERRY WHITE

Yes, you did! It was SUPERMAN!
Never mind, Boss. *I* saw it all!

Fantastic work, Lois! Well done!
Yes, fantastic!
PERRY WHITE

It's funny, Clark. You never seem to be here when Superman's about.
Maybe it's because I *am* really Superman, Lois!

Oh, Clark Kent! You are such a joker!

BOOM!
Er ... what was *that*?

Robots! They are stomping all over the city!

JIMMY!
JIMMY OLSEN ...
... GET IN HERE – NOW!

Yes, Boss?
Get me photos of those robots!
Yes, Boss!

LOIS! Write a report about the robots!
Yes, Boss!

CLARK KENT!
You can get my coffee!

KENT!
KENT?

But it looks as if Mr White will have to get his own coffee this time ...
KENT!

Robots stomping all over the city?
This sounds like a job for ...
DAILY PLANET
SUPERMAN!

Robots! What are you doing here?
Why are you smashing things?

THROW!

CATCH!
It's a good job I can catch!

Hang on, Superman!
We can help!
That's great!
But watch out … these robots are hard to beat!

SMACK!

CRASH!

Uh-oh! I was right! The robots *are* hard to beat!

But I don't give up easily.
So, come on, robots.

Bring it on!

How about a game of ...

... Throw The Robot Into Space?
Help!

Oh no, it's Jimmy Olsen! He needs help!
HELP!

STOMP!

CLICK CLICK

Luckily, Supergirl spots Jimmy just in time!
STOMP!

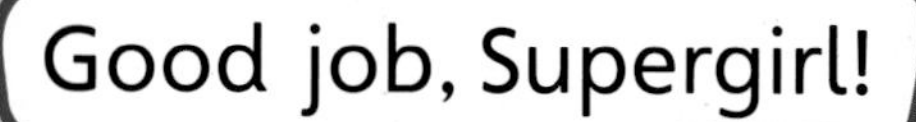

Superman puts *this* robot out of action ...

... and the Superkids sort out *this* one!

Superman quickly finishes off the other robots.
It's all over for you now, robots.
GRAB!
SNAP!
You've stomped on your last city!

Job done! Now I must get back to the newspaper.
You know, Superman *does* look a bit like Clark Kent. Could he be ...?

Puzzle Page

Use your super spotting skills to work out who is who! The answers are up the side of the page.

Answers: 1 Robot, 2 Superman, 3 Superdog, 4 Jimmy Olsen, 5 Superboy.